P9-BVH-932

Picture a Tree

Barbara Reid

North Winds Press
An imprint of Scholastic Canada Ltd.

The illustrations in this book were made with Plasticine that was shaped and pressed onto illustration board. Paint was used for special effects.

The type is set in Adobe Caslon Pro.

Photography by Ian Crysler.

Library and Archives Canada Cataloguing in Publication

Reid, Barbara, 1957-
Picture a tree / written and illustrated by Barbara Reid.

ISBN 978-1-4431-0761-7

1. Trees--Juvenile literature. 2. Picture books for children.

I. Title.

QK475.8.R45 2011   j582.16   C2011-902375-X

Copyright © 2011 by Barbara Reid.

All rights reserved.

No part of this publication may be reproduced or stored in a retrieval system, or transmitted in any form or by any means, electronic, mechanical, recording, or otherwise, without written permission of the publisher, North Winds Press, an imprint of Scholastic Canada Ltd., 604 King Street West, Toronto, Ontario M5V 1E1, Canada. In the case of photocopying or other reprographic copying, a licence must be obtained from Access Copyright (Canadian Copyright Licensing Agency), 1 Yonge Street, Suite 800, Toronto, Ontario M5E 1E5 (1-800-893-5777).

6 5 4 3 2 1   Printed in Canada 114   11 12 13 14 15

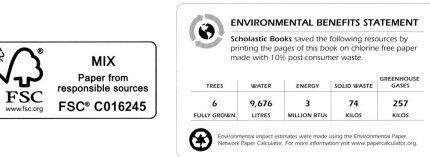

FSC
www.fsc.org

MIX
Paper from
responsible sources
FSC® C016245

ENVIRONMENTAL BENEFITS STATEMENT

Scholastic Books saved the following resources by printing the pages of this book on chlorine free paper made with 10% post-consumer waste.

TREES	WATER	ENERGY	SOLID WASTE	GREENHOUSE GASES
6	9,676	3	74	257
FULLY GROWN	LITRES	MILLION BTUs	KILOS	KILOS

Environmental impact estimates were made using the Environmental Paper Network Paper Calculator. For more information visit www.papercalculator.org.

To Ruby.

There is more than one
way to picture a tree.

3

You may see a drawing on the sky.

A game of dress-up.

7

The first drops
of colour . . .

then all the art
supplies at once.

9

A tunnel,

or an ocean.

A tree can be
a high-rise
home sweet home.

13

A pirate ship,

a bear cave,

a clubhouse,

a friend.

15

Some trees are sun umbrellas

16

on the hot walk home.

17

There are baby trees,

in-betweens,

grown-ups,

grandfathers.

You may see the end of one thing, or the start of something new.

A wild goodbye party.

A glow in the
darkness . . .

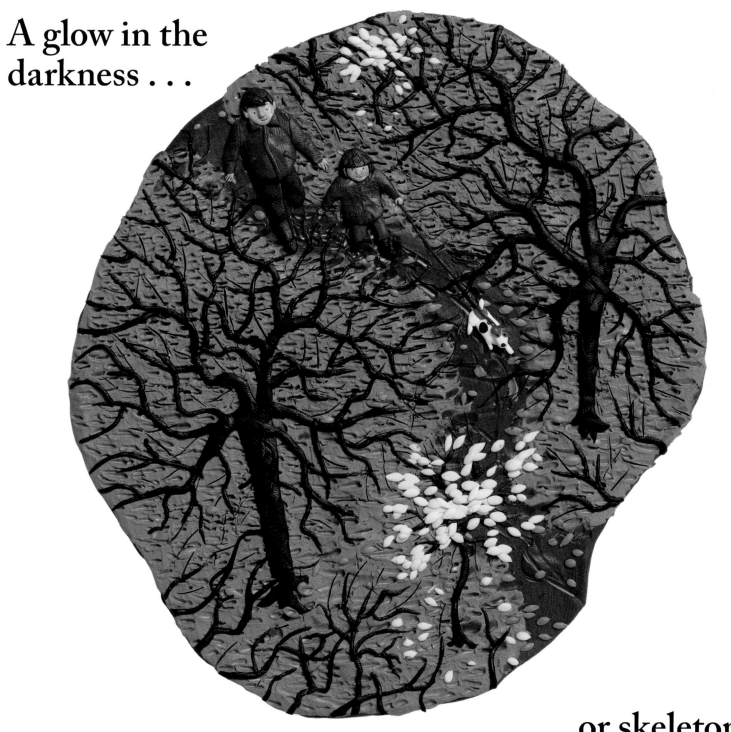

or skeletons!

Some trees put on snowsuits.

Every winter tree holds spring,

sleeping like a baby.

Picture a tree. What do *you* see?